Sylvia Bond & Richard Maher

The ROALD DAHL QUIZ BOOK 2

Illustrated by Quentin Blake

PUFFIN BOOKS

PUFFIN BOOKS

Published by the Penguin Group
Penguin Books Ltd, 27 Wrights Lane, London w8 5tz, England
Penguin Books USA Inc., 375 Hudson Street, New York, New York 10014, USA
Penguin Books Australia Ltd, Ringwood, Victoria, Australia
Penguin Books Canada Ltd, 10 Alcorn Avenue, Toronto, Ontario, Canada m4v 3b2
Penguin Books (NZ) Ltd, 182–190 Wairau Road, Auckland 10, New Zealand

Penguin Books Ltd, Registered Offices: Harmondsworth, Middlesex, England

First published 1996
5 7 9 10 8 6

The moral right of the author and illustrator has been asserted

Filmset in 14/14pt Monophoto Palatino

Set by Datix International Limited, Bungay, Suffolk
Made and printed in England by Clays Ltd, St Ives plc

Contents

For Paul, Peter, Brian and Aoife

Acknowledgements

I wish to thank my parents, John and Catherine Bond, for their support and encouragement, and particularly for their help with the children.

Thanks also to my helpers, who included Paula Geraghty, Sarah Marks, Paul and Peter Maher, Orlaith Sheehy and Rachel Barret, all of whom checked a chapter for me, and to Dan Loughrey and Andrew Flynn for proof-reading.

Apologies to author Maeve Binchy, whose name was spelt incorrectly in the first Quiz Book. Maeve has given me great support and encouragement and I am very appreciative of this.

My thanks to Damien Murphy and David Kane, both of whom were of great assistance with computer hitches. Also to Sharon O'Toole and Bernadette Harrington, who came to the rescue when my typing speed was holding things up!

Finally, I wish to thank my husband, W. Richard Maher. This book was his brainchild, and he spent many hours in the tedium of isolation in hospital composing amusing questions to entertain the children he loved. In his memory, I have completed the work he started, which we shared together, and which became the symbol of the joy that life can hold, even in the worst of circumstances.

Questions

Revolting Rhymes

Cinderella

1   For which two reasons was the real story changed?
a) To keep the names of the family secret
b) Because the real one was much more gory
c) To keep the children happy

2   Why was the prince turned to pulp?
a) Because the two ugly sisters jumped on him
b) Because the beautiful Cinderella danced with him
c) Because the footman slipped and dropped a huge barrel full of beer right on top of him

3   How was Cinderella dressed leaving the ball?
a) In the wonderful gown given to her by her Fairy Godmother
b) In her underwear
c) In her old ragged dress

4   What happened to the dainty shoe?
   a) The prince let it fall and shatter into a thousand pieces
   b) A magpie carried it away
   c) It was flushed down the loo

5   How did the prince get out of marrying the ugly sister whose face was blotched with blisters?
   a) He offered her one million pounds
   b) He convinced his cousin to marry her instead
   c) He chopped off her head

6   What did the prince do to the other ugly sister?
   a) He chased her round the room
   b) He sang to her
   c) He chopped off her head

7   What did the prince say when he saw Cindy?
   a) 'Darling!'
   b) 'At last! My dream has come true!'
   c) 'Off with her nut!'

8   Whom did Cinderella decide to marry?
   a) The prince's brother, who was much more handsome and kind anyway
   b) A decent man
   c) The footman — she liked him

Jack and the Beanstalk

1   How old was the cow?
   a) As old as billy-o
   b) As old as really old cheese
   c) As old as the man in the moon

2   What colour did Jack's mother turn when she
saw what Jack had sold the cow for?
   a) Boiling hot red
   b) Plain green
   c) Sickly yellow

3   What did Jack's mother do with the bean?
   a) She threw it on the compost heap
   b) She threw it on the rubbish dump
   *c) She squashed it with her foot and flicked it out of
   the window*

4   What did Jack's mother do to him for selling
Daisy for a bean?
   *a) She beat him with the handle of the vacuum
   cleaner*
   b) She made him take the bean back
   *c) She thanked him and waited for something magic
   to happen*

5   What was on the top of the beanstalk?
   a) A golden harp
   b) A giant with a clever nose
   c) An Englishman

6   What happened to Jack's mum?
   a) She climbed the beanstalk herself and got the gold
   *b) She knocked the giant out with the handle of the
   vacuum cleaner*
   c) She was eaten by the giant

7   What was Jack's only hope if he was to get the
golden leaves?
   a) That the giant had a cold
   *b) To cover himself from head to foot with sweet-
   smelling flowers*
   c) A bath

8   Which of the following did Jack not do?
   a) Brush his teeth
   b) Blow his nose
   c) Clean between his toes
   d) Go out smelling like a rose

Snow-White and the Seven Dwarfs

1   How did Snow-White's father find a new wife?
a) He invited every fair lady in the land to a ball
b) He put advertisements in every magazine
c) They met on a TV dating show

2   What was the curious toy of the new Queen?
a) A Chinese cabinet full of secret compartments
b) A robot which followed her everywhere
c) A magic, talking looking-glass

3   What was the most awful day for the Queen?
a) The day she turned forty
b) The day the thistle soup landed in her lap
c) The day she became number two

4   What did the Queen plan to do with Snow-White?
   a) *Have her rotten guts for dinner*
   b) *Have her bleeding heart cut out*
   c) *Both a) and b)*

5   What did Snow-White do when the huntsman let her go?
   a) *She found a cottage in the woods*
   b) *She hitched a ride into the city*
   c) *She made her way back to the palace*

6   What work did Snow-White find?
   a) *Personal secretary to the president of the Bank of England*
   b) *General cook and parlour-maid*
   c) *Assistant in a bookie's office*

7   What vice did Snow-White's employers have?
   a) *They gambled*
   b) *They smoked*
   c) *They drank too much*

8   Were the dwarfs still very poor?
   a) *Yes — gambling never pays*
   b) *No — they were millionaires*
   c) *No — they all married ladies with plenty of money*

17

Goldilocks and the Three Bears

1 What is the story of Goldilocks really all
about?
 a) A little girl who got lost in the woods
 b) A brazen little crook
 c) How mankind and nature get along

2 At what time are men seldom at their prime?
 a) Most of the time
 b) Breakfast-time
 c) Evening-time

3 What does Roald Dahl call Goldilocks?
 a) A nosey thieving little louse
 b) A pot-bellied blabbermouth
 c) Both a) and b)

4 What did mammy bear collect?
 a) China thimbles
 b) Porcelain statues
 c) Antiques

5   What style was baby bear's chair?
    a) *Chippendale*
    b) *Elizabethan*
    c) *Edwardian*

6   What did Goldie say when she broke the chair?
    a) *'Oh, dear! Oh, heavens! What a shame!'*
    b) *'What a lousy chair!'*
    c) *Both a) and b)*

7   What was the really horrid thing on the heel
of Goldie's shoe as she got into bed?
    a) *A sticky lump of porridge*
    b) *Something that a dog had done*
    c) *A blob of jam*

8   What sticky end does Goldie deserve?
    a) *To fall into a huge cauldron of cold porridge*
    b) *To have baby bear eat her up to get his porridge
    back*
    c) *To have the bears cover her with honey and then
    lick her clean*

Little Red Riding Hood and the Wolf

1   What did Wolf do when he felt hungry?
   a) He ate wild strawberries and blueberries
   b) He went and knocked on Grandma's door
   *c) He followed Little Red Riding Hood through the
   wood*

2   What did Grandmamma taste like?
   a) She was tough
   b) She was tender and lean
   c) She was too dry

3   Why was Wolf yelping around the kitchen?
   a) He hadn't had enough to eat
   b) He wanted second helpings
   c) Both a) and b)

4   What did Wolf think Little Red Riding Hood would taste like?
a) Peaches and cream
b) Caviare
c) Sausage and mash

5   What did Little Red Riding Hood forget to say?
a) What big teeth you have
b) What big eyes you have
c) What big ears you have

6   When did Little Red Riding Hood's eyelid flicker?
a) When Wolf was about to lick her
b) When the plot was getting thicker
c) Before she whipped the pistol from her knickers

7   What new look did Little Red Riding Hood have?
a) A trimming of wolf fur on her hood
b) A lovely furry wolfskin coat
c) A tie-dyed wolfskin leotard

The Three Little Pigs

1   What kind of pig do you meet only now and then?
   a) A pig who is a fool
   b) A pig who is clever
   c) A pig who wears a wig

2   What piece of the pig did Wolfie keep till last?
   a) The delicate ears
   b) The tail
   c) The trotters

3   Why did Wolfie keep eating, even though his tummy was full?
   a) He was storing food for a lean day
   b) He simply liked indulging
   c) He was a greedy pig

4   What was different about Piggy Number
Three?
   a) He was bright and brainy
   b) He was a friend of the huntsman
   c) He came from a different family of pigs

5   What would Wolf do if he couldn't blow
Pig's house down?
   a) He'd blow it up
   b) He'd get a breaking-ball
   c) He'd try the next house

6   Who did Piggy call to help?
   a) The huntsman
   b) The police
   c) Miss Red Riding Hood

7   What delayed Miss Hood in coming to Pig's
rescue?
   a) She had just begun to wash her hair
   b) She was just putting away her shopping
   c) She had just stepped out of the bath

8   What was dripping from Wolf's jaw?
   a) Spit
   b) Blood
   c) Mayonnaise

Dirty Beasts

The Pig

1 Where did Pig live?
  a) England
  b) France
  c) Wales

2 What question drove clever Piggy round the bend?
  a) What life was really all about
  b) What made an aeroplane fly
  c) What made the sun shine

3 What part of Piggy would cost the most?
  a) The tender juicy chops
  b) The bacon to sell slice by slice
  c) The pork to make a roast

4   What was the name of the Farmer?
    a) Farmer Bland
    b) Farmer Bloggs
    c) Farmer Hogg

5   What did Piggy do to the Farmer?
    a) He sliced him up like bacon
    b) He ate him up from head to toe
    c) He flattened him like a steamroller

6   How long did it take Piggy to eat as far as the Farmer's feet?
    a) Twenty-four hours
    b) Two hours
    c) An hour

7   Why did Pig eat the Farmer first?
    a) Because he had gone right off pigswill
    b) Because he just felt like it
    c) Because he feared the worst

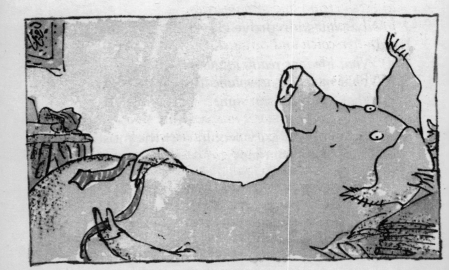

The Crocodile

1   How many children does Crocky-Wock eat on Saturdays?
   a) *Nine baked in a crumble pie*
   b) *Six juicy children*
   c) *Seven baked in sausage rolls*

2   How many boys and girls does he especially enjoy?
   a) *Four girls, two boys*
   b) *Two girls, four boys*
   c) *Three of each*

3   What does Crocky-Wock smear the boys with?
   a) *Mustard*
   b) *Tomato sauce*
   c) *Burger relish*

4   What goes extremely well with plaits and curls?
   a) *Fresh cream and strawberries*
   b) *Chocolate fudge mallows*
   c) *Butterscotch and caramel*

5   What is a super marvellous treat for Crocky-Wock?
   a) *When girls are sweet and boys are sour*
   b) *When boys are hot and girls are sweet*
   c) *When he makes a boy–girl casserole special*

6   What colour is Crocky-Wock's skin?
    a) Rotsome reddish
    b) Yucky yellow
    c) Greasy greenish

The Lion

1   What did the lion like to eat?
    a) A whole zebra
    b) An antelope
    c) A lot of red and tender meat

2   What does the lion prefer to steak and chops?
    a) You
    b) Roast of lamb
    c) Carved beef or devilled ham

30

The Scorpion

1   What is the scorpion's name?
   a) Stingaling
   b) Stingalong
   c) Stingalot

2   Where is it said you will never find a scorpion in your bed?
   a) Iceland
   b) Italy
   c) England

3   What type of a face does the scorpion have?
   a) Scowling and murderous
   b) Vicious and full of vice
   c) Scabby and scary

4   With what does the scorpion sting you?
   a) His sharp and jagged claw
   b) His long and pointed claw
   c) His long and crinkly tail

5   Where does the scorpion wish to sting you?
   a) Upon your rump
   b) On your thigh
   c) On the bottom of your foot

The Ant-Eater

1   What was the worst thing of all about Roy?
   a) He was most dreadfully spoiled
   b) He was half baked and half boiled
   c) He was a plump and unattractive boy

2   What did Roy want that he had not got?
   a) His own theme park
   b) A giant ant-eater
   c) His own fast-food chain

3   Who lived near Delhi in a tent?
   a) An Indian gent
   b) A tiny man with a great big belly
   c) The chief of the Foreign Legion

4   What did the ant-eater ask Roy for?
   a) Some red ants
   b) A bit of meat
   c) Some black ants

5   What did the ant-eater do to Roy's aunt?
    a) He wagged his tail and snuggled up to her
    b) He ate her
    c) He leapt up and landed in her lap

6   What did the ant-eater do to Roy?
    a) He mulched him
    b) He regurgitated him
    c) He had him for dessert

The Porcupine

1   What day did the girl get her pocket money?
    a) Saturday
    b) Friday
    c) Sunday

2   What did the girl buy with her pocket money?
    a) A kilo of broken toffee
    b) A great big bag of raspberry creams
    c) The most gorgeous rainbow-coloured marbles ever

3   The Porcupine punctured her in the tender little rump
    True or false?

4   Where did her mum take her to have the prickles removed?
   a) The doctor
   b) The garage
   c) The dentist

5   What did Mr Myers charge for removing the porcupine quills?
   a) Fifty guineas
   b) Forty-five pounds
   c) A dollar for every quill pulled

The Cow

1   What was the name of the cow?
   a) Miss Milky Daisy
   b) Miss Moo
   c) Miss Jersey Cream

2   What was unusual about this cow?
   a) She had only one horn
   b) She had no tail at all
   c) She had two lumps quite near her rump

3   Why did millions come each day to stare at the wondrous cow?
   a) She gave fifty gallons of milk per hour
   b) She could moo along to any song you cared to mention
   c) She had a pair of gold and silver wings

4   Where had the horrid man in the crowd
travelled from?
   a) Afghanistan
   b) Bangkok
   c) Timbuktu

5   What did Daisy do to the 'silly foreign freak'?
   a) She whizzed by and knocked off his wig
   b) She gave him a left hook and knocked out his
   teeth
   c) She dropped a cowpat on his head

The Toad and the Snail

1   How big was the giant toad?
   a) As large as a fair-sized fattish pig
   b) As large as the calf of a cow
   c) As large as a sizeable sheep

2   What did the giant toad invite the boy to do?
   a) To hear him sing an aria
   b) To paddle in the pond
   c) To take a ride on his back

3   Where did the toad and the boy stop for tea?
   a) Above the Cliffs of Dover
   b) On the promenade in Brighton
   c) At the Cliff Café in Land's End

4   What do the French think is absolutely
ripping?
   a) *To guzzle frogs-legs fried in dripping*
   b) *To drink frog soup by gently sipping*
   c) *To eat the toads while they're still flipping*

5   What did the toad become?
   a) *A giant man-eater*
   b) *A stupendous mountain-ox*
   c) *A wonderfully enormous snail*

6   What did the snail transform into?
   a) *A four-winged weather bird*
   b) *The enchanting Roly-Poly Bird*
   c) *A hang-glider*

The Tummy Beast

1 What does the tummy beast demand for tea?
   a) Sugar buns
   b) Curried beef
   c) Chocolate cake

2 What does the tummy beast say is not a sin?
   a) To be a greedy guzzling glutton
   b) To raid the biscuit tin
   c) To tell a lie

3 What did the tummy beast want lots of?
   a) Nuts
   b) Chocs and sweets
   c) Both a) and b)

4 What did the tummy beast threaten to do if he didn't get what he wanted?
   a) He said he would choke the boy
   b) He said he would twist the boy's guts
   c) He said he would scream non-stop

5 What did the boy's mother do when she heard the tummy beast?
   a) She fainted
   b) She had hyper-hysterics
   c) She took no notice

The Magic Finger

1   How many children live on the Gregg farm?
   a) Two
   b) Three
   c) Four

2   What are the names of the boys?
   a) Peter and Brian
   b) Paul and Richard
   c) Philip and William

3   What did they shoot?
   a) Animals and birds
   b) Clay pigeons
   c) Old tin cans

4   What did the Greggs do when the girl tried to
stop them hunting?
   a) They laughed
   b) They walked past her
   c) Both a) and b)

5   What were they carrying
coming out of the woods
that made the girl so cross?
   a) Six rabbits
   b) A young deer
   c) Ten pheasants

6   What did the Greggs do when the girl started shouting at them?
   a) The boys laughed and made faces
   b) Mr Gregg told her to go home and mind her own P's and Q's
   c) Both a) and b)

7   What happened to Mrs Winter, the teacher?
   a) She grew whiskers and a tail
   b) She grew rabbit's ears and a bunny tail
   c) She grew feathers and a beak

8   Will the magic finger ever be taken off Mrs Winter?
   a) Yes, once a year
   b) No, never at all
   c) If she asks nicely

9   When does the magic finger start to work?
   a) *Every time there is a full moon*
   b) *Every time the girl cuts her fingernails*
   c) *When the girl gets cross and sees red*

10   What does the girl feel when the magic finger
starts?
   a) *She feels hot all over and the tip of her forefinger*
   tingles
   b) *A quick flash comes out of her, like something*
   electric
   c) *Both a) and b)*

11   How many ducks did the Greggs catch in two
hours?
   a) *Sixteen*
   b) *Twenty*
   c) *Twenty-four*

12   What did the ducks do to the Greggs on the
way home?
   a) *They kept dropping droppings on them*
   b) *They kept flying around and around, following*
   them
   c) *They kept making nose dives and sweeping around*
   their legs

13   Why did Mr Gregg go out of the house at
night?
   a) *To check that the garage was locked*
   b) *To see that the hens were safe*
   c) *To get firewood*

14 Why did he go back to the house quickly?
 a) Because he was frightened of the dark
 b) Because four ducks were flying around and around the house
 c) Because a huge thunderstorm was coming

15 What happened when the Greggs woke up?
 a) Mr Gregg could not find his hands
 b) Mrs Gregg had grown wings
 c) Both a) and b)

16 What size was Mr Gregg?
 a) He was the size of a tiny little man
 b) He was the size of a plump Christmas turkey
 c) He was the size of a hen

17 Why could Mrs Gregg not look at herself in the mirror?
 a) She couldn't put on her glasses now she had wings
 b) She was not tall enough to see into it
 c) Mr Gregg wouldn't move away from it

18   What size were the boys?
   a) They were about as big as robins
   b) They were the size of turtle doves
   c) They were as small as young chicks

19   How did the Gregg family get out of the house?
   a) They flew out of the window
   b) They ran through the cat-flap
   c) They walked out of the front door

20   What did the Greggs see in their garden?
   a) A whole army of ducks
   b) Four enormous ducks with arms
   c) All the animals of the wood gathered in the farmyard

21   What was Philip afraid would happen to them in the night?
   a) That they would fall off the branches when they were asleep
   b) That an owl might attack them
   c) That they would be eaten by cats and foxes

22   What did Mr Gregg decide to build?
   a) A den
   b) A nest
   c) A burrow

23 How did they gather the material for their safe place?
  a) *With their mouths*
  b) *With their toes*
  c) *Both a) and b)*

24 What did they use to soften their safe place?
  a) *Leaves and feathers*
  b) *Toilet tissue*
  c) *Grass*

25 What did Mrs Gregg say when she tried sitting in the nest?
  a) *'Oh, this won't do at all'*
  b) *'I suppose it will have to do'*
  c) *'I feel I might lay an egg any moment'*

26 What did Philip think was the advantage of being so high up?
  a) *That nobody could hurt them*
  b) *That they could see a long way*
  c) *That they could play with other birds*

27   What food did they plan to take from the house?
   a) Some corn
   b) A tin of biscuits
   c) A few slices of bread

28   How did they plan to get the food?
   a) They would fly in through the window when the ducks were not looking
   b) They would sneak in through the cat-flap
   c) They would go to the storehouse in the barn

29   What happened when they tried to get into the house?
   a) The big duck fired at them
   b) All the windows and doors were closed
   c) The ducks laughed at them

30   What was Mrs Gregg going to make for dinner?
   a) Slugburgers
   b) Wormburgers
   c) Both a) and b)

31   What did they try to eat from their own garden?
   a) Gooseberries
   b) Apples
   c) Rhubarb

32 Why was it a bad night in the nest?
   a) They were all starving
   b) They were all sitting on top of each other
   c) A great wind began to blow and it rained all
   night

33 What gave Mr Gregg the surprise of his life?
   a) Seeing the ducks pointing guns at him and his family
   b) Realizing that his wings were still and he couldn't
   fly
   c) Finding that he actually enjoyed worms

34   How many of the duck's chicks had Mr Gregg
shot?
   a) Five
   b) Four
   c) Six

35   What did Mr Gregg promise the ducks?
   a) That he would never shoot a single duck again
   b) That he would never shoot anything else again
   c) Both a) and b)

36   What did the duck congratulate Mr Gregg on?
   a) His wise decision
   b) The nest
   c) His fine family

37   How did the Greggs get back to normal?
   *a) Everything went black and a funny feeling came
   over them and they heard a great wind blowing*
   *b) The black turned to blue, to green, to red and then
   to gold, and they were standing in sunshine*
   c) Both a) and b)

38   What did Philip and William do once
everyone realized that their arms were back and
they were not tiny any more?
   a) They started to wrestle
   b) They danced with joy
   c) They hugged each other

39   What did they see high above their heads
when they were back to normal?
   a) A flock of starlings
   b) Big black rainclouds
   c) Four wild ducks

40   What did the girl see when she walked into
the Greggs' garden?
   a) Mr Gregg breaking guns with a huge hammer
   b) Mrs Gregg putting flowers on tiny mounds
   c) Both a) and b)

41   What were Philip and William doing in the middle of the yard?
   a) Playing cricket
   b) Feeding birds
   c) Fighting

42   What new name did Mr and Mrs Gregg take?
   a) Mr and Mrs Duck
   b) Mr and Mrs Egg
   c) Mr and Mrs Drake

43   What did William show the girl to prove that the story was true?
   a) The feathers all over the place
   b) The broken guns
   c) The nest

44   What did Mrs Gregg offer as proof of the truth of the story?
   a) A collection of duck feathers
   b) The mess in the bathroom
   c) The fact that she still felt like laying an egg

45   What sound did they all hear from near the lake?
   a) Wild animals screaming
   b) A loud bang
   c) A duck family passing by

46   What happened to the girl when she heard
the sound of someone hunting?
   a) She froze and went stiff all over
   b) Her hair stood on end
   c) The tip of her finger began tingling

47   What did she say about the Coopers as she
ran towards the lake?
   a) That they would be nesting in trees that night
   b) That she hoped they would enjoy slugburgers
   c) That she hoped they liked flying

The Twits

1 What is the first question Roald Dahl asks himself about men with hairy faces?
   a) How often do they wash their faces
   b) How do the ones with curly beards get them to stay curly
   c) How do the ones with great moustaches make sure they are clean

2 Which parts of Mr Twit's face were not covered with thick hair?
   a) His forehead, eyes and nose
   b) His nostrils and ear-holes
   c) Both a) and b)

3 How did Mr Twit feel his hairiness made him look?
   a) Terrifically wise and grand
   b) Exceptionally distinctive
   c) Like a professor

4 What was Mr Twit at the age of sixty?
   a) Recently retired
   b) The holder of the 'hairiest man in the world' title
   c) A bigger twit than ever

5 How did Mr Twit's beard grow?
   a) Smooth and matted
   b) In spikes, like the bristles of a nailbrush
   c) Like a horse-hair brush

6 How often did Mr Twit wash his face?
   a) Never
   b) Only on Sundays
   c) Once a year

7 What is so different about people with beards?
   a) They cannot eat anything without leaving some of the food clinging to the hairs
   b) They never laugh
   c) They always shout

8   What would Mr Twit find if he explored the
hairy jungle around his mouth?
   a) *Maggoty green cheese and a mouldy old cornflake*
   b) *The slimy tail of a tinned sardine and some minced
   chicken-livers*
   c) *Both a) and b)*

9   What was Mr Twit?
   a) *A dainty eater*
   b) *A foul and smelly old man, who was also
   extremely horrid*
   c) *A lovely person to be with*

10   How had Mrs Twit become ugly?
   a) *She was born ugly*
   b) *She had ugly thoughts*
   c) *She had a nasty accident*

11   Why did Mrs Twit carry a walking-stick?
   a) *Because she had a false leg*
   b) *Because she had warts on the sole of her left foot*
   c) *So that she could hit things with it*

12   What was unusual about Mrs Twit's eyes?
   a) She was cross-eyed
   b) They were two different colours
   *c) She had a glass eye that was always looking the
   other way*

13   What did Mr Twit find at the bottom of his
mug of beer?
   a) A shrivelled slimy worm
   b) Mrs Twit's glass eye
   c) A set of false teeth

14   How did Mr Twit pay back Mrs Twit for the
beer-mug trick?
   a) He put a large frog in her bed
   b) He put a Giant Skillywiggler in her bed
   *c) He put six slimy, slithering snakes between her
   sheets*

15   What did Mrs Twit do?
   a) She fainted
   b) She rolled over on her side and went to sleep
   c) She turned the bed inside-out

16   How did Mrs Twit pay back Mr Twit for the slimy-thing-in-the-bed trick?
   a) She put glue on his toothbrush
   b) She made Squiggly Spaghetti, with worms
   c) She put itching powder in his socks

17   What was Mr Twit's nasty trick with the walking-stick?
   a) He put little extra pieces on to the end of her walking-stick
   b) He cut tiny pieces off her walking-stick every night
   c) He changed the walking-stick for a rubber one that kept wobbling

18 How did Mr Twit cure Mrs Twit of the
shrinks?
   *a) He got two tug-of-war teams to use Mrs Twit as
   a rope*
   b) He used an old-fashioned stretching machine
   *c) He tied her feet down and attached sixty gas-filled
   balloons to the top half of her body*

19 Who gave Mr Twit the idea to get rid of Mrs
Twit?
   a) Mrs Twit
   b) It was his own idea
   c) He got it from a magazine

20 How did Mrs Twit return to solid ground?
   *a) Pecking birds burst the balloons and she plunged
   down*
   *b) She bit through their strings and slowly released
   the balloons so she could float down*
   *c) A sudden burst of fireworks frizzled the balloons
   like sausages and she shot back down again*

21 What was the fiery fury that landed on Mr
Twit?
   a) A chimney pot
   b) Mrs Twit herself
   c) A falling star

22 What was unusual about the Twits' house?
   a) It had no windows
   b) It was surrounded by barbed wire
   c) It had a thatched roof

23 What was Mrs Twit's garden like?
  a) Full of useful vegetables
  b) Surprisingly neat and tidy
  c) A mass of thistles and stinging-nettles

24 What did the Twits eat on Wednesdays?
  a) Nettle soup
  b) Bird Pie
  c) Thistle surprise

25 What did Mr Twit use Hugtight glue for?
  a) For repairing all the broken things about the house
  b) For playing tricks on Mrs Twit
  c) For catching birds

26 What did Mr Twit find stuck on The Big Dead Tree?
  a) Four little boys
  b) Five little squirrels
  c) Six little monkeys

27 How did they escape?
  a) The branch broke and hit Mr Twit on the head, knocking him out
  b) They slipped out of their pants and tumbled to the ground
  c) They shouted until help arrived

28   What was Mr Twit's dream?
  a) Catching a turkey on The Big Dead Tree
  b) To own an upside-down monkey circus
  c) To win the 'beard of the year' contest

29   What was the most difficult thing to do upside-down?
  a) To play football
  b) To dance
  c) To eat and drink

30   What did Muggle-Wump and his family long for?
  a) To escape from the cage
  b) To return to the African jungle
  c) Both a) and b)

31   Where did the Roly-Poly Bird come from?
  a) Africa
  b) South America
  c) Malaysia

32   What did the monkeys ask the Roly-Poly Bird to do?
  a) To let them out of their cage
  b) To warn the other birds about The Big Dead Tree glue
  c) To sing them a song from the old country

33 What trick did Mr Twit play to get the birds?
   a) He painted the tree again with glue
   b) He painted the cage with glue
   c) Both a) and b)

34 What did Mr and Mrs Twit do after two days without Bird Pie?
   a) They went to buy shotguns
   b) They put poison in the birdseed
   c) They put a mirror on the roof to confuse the birds

35 Who got the key to the door of the cage?
   a) The four boys
   b) The Roly-Poly Bird
   c) The smallest baby squeezed out and got it

36 What was Muggle-Wump's plan to pay the Twits back?
   a) To make them stand upside-down for hours and hours
   b) To put Hugtight glue all over the door handle
   c) To get all of the birds to attack them

37 What was the first move of the plan?
  a) To cover the ceiling with glue
  b) To have a feast of food in the kitchen
  c) To paint everything in the bathroom

38 What did the Roly-Poly Bird think of
Muggle-Wump when he heard the plan?
  a) 'He's wacky!'
  b) 'Poor old Muggles has gone off his wump'
  c) Both a) and b)

39 How were they able to stick heavy furniture
on to the ceiling?
  *a) By using Hugtight glue, the strongest glue in the
  world*
  b) By using a hammer and nails
  c) By using a clamp from the shed

40   What was the finishing touch to transform the Twits' living-room?
  a) Fixing ashtrays to the ceiling
  b) Arranging the beastly plastic gnome on the sideboard
  c) Turning all the pictures upside-down

41   Why didn't the Twits start shooting as soon as they came back?
  a) Mrs Twit had to practise first
  b) They had to go inside to load up the guns
  c) They wanted something to eat first

42   What did the ravens drop on the Twits' heads?
  a) Their dirty droppings
  b) Hugtight glue
  c) Some feathers

43   Whose idea was it to stand on their heads?
  a) Mr Twit
  b) Mrs Twit
  c) Both a) and b)

44   What did the Muggle-Wump family build in the tallest tree?
  a) A nest
  b) A tree-house
  c) Nothing at all

45 How did the birds help the Muggle-Wump family?

   a) *They built their nests around the tree-house to conceal it*

   b) *They brought food for them*

   c) *They mounted a guard to watch out for the Twits*

46 How did the Muggle-Wump family get back to Africa?

a) *They joined a circus which travelled to Africa*
b) *They stowed away on an Air-Africa flight*
c) *They flew Roly-Poly Super Jet*

47 What happened to Mr Twit's head?

a) *It disappeared into the fatty folds of his flabby neck*
b) *It became flattened and very wide*
c) *It became wrinkled like an accordion*

48   What finally happened to the Twits?
  a) They were rescued by the postman
  b) They were found by the RSPCA — the Royal
  Society for the Prevention of Cruelty to Animals
  c) They got the Dreaded Shrinks and disappeared

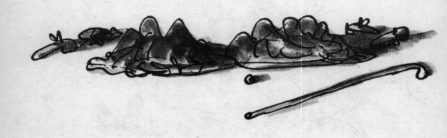

49   Who discovered what was left of the Twits?
  a) Peter, the postman
  b) Fred, the gas-meter reader
  c) Judy, the junk-yard collector

50   What did everyone, including Fred, shout
when the Twits were gone?
  a) 'Hallelujah!'
  b) 'Saints be praised!'
  c) 'Hooray!'

James and the Giant Peach

1　How old was James Henry Trotter when his parents were killed?
　　a) He was two
　　b) He was four
　　c) He was five

2　How were his parents killed?
　　a) They were involved in a terrible car crash
　　b) They were stampeded by a herd of gnu
　　c) They were eaten up by an enormous angry rhinoceros

3　What was so special about where James lived with his parents?
　　a) It was by the sea
　　b) It was in a vast stretch of open countryside
　　c) It was on top of a high mountain

4　What were the names of James's aunts?
　　a) Aunt Dilly and Aunt Dotty
　　b) Aunt Sponge and Aunt Spiker
　　c) Aunt Whinge and Aunt Whine

5　What kind of people were his aunts?
　　a) They were selfish and lazy and cruel
　　b) They were wild and weird and wonderful
　　c) They were kind and gentle and loving

6   What did Aunt Sponge look like?
   a) She was enormously fat and very short
   b) She was like a great white soggy overboiled
   cabbage
   c) Both a) and b)

7   What did Aunt Spiker look like?
   a) She had short spiky hair
   b) She was lean and tall and bony
   c) Both a) and b)

8   What came out of the laurel bushes?
   a) A lively little leprechaun
   b) A small old man in a dark-green suit
   c) A woodland elf who had lost his wood

9   What was in the paper bag given to James?
   a) Things that looked like blue beans which were
   magic
   b) Things that looked like golden coins which glittered
   and glowed
   c) Things that looked like green stones or crystals
   which were made of crocodile tongues

10   What final ingredient was James instructed to
add to the jug of water and the contents of the
bag?
   a) The eyeballs of a lizard
   b) Nail parings from Aunt Sponge and Aunt Spiker
   c) Ten hairs from his own head

11   What did James do with the magical contents
of the paper bag?
   *a) He spilled them all over the place when he fell flat
   on his face*
   b) He poured them over Aunt Sponge and Aunt Spiker
   *c) He ran straight to the house and followed the
   instructions*

12   Where did the crocodile tongues disappear?
   a) Down into the earth round the peach tree
   b) Into thin air
   c) Down the well

13 Who was first to notice the peach growing?
  a) Aunt Sponge
  b) Aunt Spiker
  c) James

14 What did Aunt Sponge cry out when she saw how big the peach had grown?
  a) 'Hallelujah and how's your hairy uncle!'
  b) 'Terrifico! Magnifico! Splendifico!'
  c) Both a) and b)

15 How much did the aunts charge per person to see the magnificent peach?
  a) Fifty pence
  b) One pound
  c) One shilling

16 Where was James when all the people came to see the peach?
  a) Helping to sell tickets
  b) Playing with the children
  c) Locked up in his bedroom

17 What did the aunts do to James when the people had all gone?
  a) They ordered him to go outside to clean up all the rubbish people had left behind
  b) They gave him bread and water and kept him out of the way while they counted their money
  c) They gave him the leftovers for his tea

18   How did James feel alone in the dark outside?
  a) He was scared
  b) He felt little shivers of excitement
  c) Both a) and b)

19   How did James get inside the stone at the centre of the peach?
  a) Through a door at the end of a tunnel
  b) On a rope hanging down from the stem
  c) On a ladder of silk spun by silkworms

20   What was so strange about the insect-creatures?
  a) They were as big as James himself
  b) They had all become transparent and multicoloured
  c) They were all sparkling and glittering green like emeralds

21   Why, when he saw the insects, was James absolutely terrified?
   a) He was allergic to insects
   b) He thought, when they said they were hungry, that they wanted to eat him
   c) He was afraid they would tread on him

22   What sent the Centipede into hysterics?
   a) The Ladybird telling him to stop pulling the Earthworm's leg
   b) The Old-Green-Grasshopper saying he was a musician, not a pest
   c) Hurling his boot at the Glow-worm to make her turn out the light

23   Who made the beds?
   a) The Silkworm
   b) The Spider
   c) James

24   What are Glow-worms like?
   a) Ordinary worms with a glowing end
   b) Lady fireflies without wings
   c) Wasps with luminous tails

25   What made the peach start to move?
   a) The Centipede nibbled away the stem
   b) The weight of the peach leaning over the hill broke the stem off the tree
   c) Everyone inside began to dance and jump

26 What happened to Aunt Sponge and Aunt Spiker?
  a) With a crunch, they were ironed out as flat as a couple of paper dolls
  b) They were arrested for taking money under false pretences
  c) They skipped for joy because James was gone

27 When did the peach finally stop rolling?
  a) When it went through the wall of a famous chocolate factory
  b) When it crashed through herds of cows and ran into a pigsty
  c) When, with a loud smack, it hit the water

28 Who thought they would all starve to death so far away from the land?
  a) The Earthworm
  b) The Centipede
  c) The Old-Green-Grasshopper

29 What was the first truly terrible thing that happened to the peach?
  a) It was badly bruised by an iceberg
  b) It was attacked by sharks
  c) The skin shrivelled in the sun

30 How did James plan to rescue the peach?
  a) By lifting it out of the water
  b) By getting the Spider to weave a waterproof web around it
  c) By getting the Centipede to pour poison all over the skin

31 How many seagulls did they need for the plan?
  a) Four hundred and forty-four
  b) Five hundred and two
  c) Nine hundred and ninety-nine

32 What was the name of the ship which witnessed the peach in the sky?
  a) Marie Céleste
  b) QE2
  c) Queen Mary

33 What instrument did the Old-Green-Grasshopper say he was?
  a) A violin
  b) A banjo
  c) A celestial cello

34 Where does the Old-Green-Grasshopper keep his ears?
  a) On his head of course
  b) One on each side of his tummy
  c) One on each front leg, just below the knee

35   What were the tall, wispy, wraithlike, shadowy, white creatures they met at night?
   a) Millions of ghosts who were lost
   b) Cloud-icebergs in the sky
   c) Cloud-Men

36   What caused these strange creatures to notice the peach?
   a) The Old-Green-Grasshopper's music
   b) The Centipede's insults
   c) The fresh, fruity, juicy scent of the peach

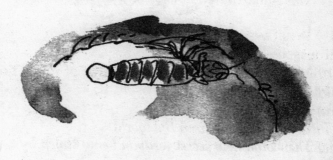

37   Why could the Glow-worm not put on her light?
   a) Her battery needed recharging
   b) Her bulb was broken
   c) She was far too exhausted and had no energy left

38   What were the second group of terrible creatures doing in the clouds?
   a) Painting a rainbow
   b) Having a great cloud-ball fight
   c) Skiing down the slopes of the cloud

39   What disaster befell the Centipede?
   a) Twenty-three of his shoes fell off the peach
   b) He was entirely covered by a gallon of thick purple paint
   c) Both a) and b)

40   What did the people of the City of New York think the peach was?
   a) An alien spacecraft
   b) The biggest bomb in the world
   c) Their own new secret weapon being stolen by enemies

41   Where did the peach land?
   a) On to the pinnacle of the Empire State Building
   b) In the lake in Central Park
   c) On the emergency runway at JFK airport

42   What happened when the Old-Green-Grasshopper stuck his head out?
   a) Six big strong men fainted
   b) The Chief of Police swallowed his megaphone
   c) The fire-engine's ladder crashed into the peach

43   What stopped the panic among the men?
   a) The Old-Green-Grasshopper started playing his
   violin
   b) James appeared and said, 'Hello, everybody!'
   c) Both a) and b)

44   Why was the Mayor's limousine skidding all
over the place?
   a) Because the Mayor was drunk as a lord
   b) Because the driver couldn't see through all the
   ticker-tape
   c) Because juice was leaking out from the peach and
   spilling on to the road

45   How was the peach completely eaten?
   a) Free slices on paper plates were handed to everyone
   on the road
   b) Millions of ants ate through it in seconds
   c) A long trail of children ate the peach to their hearts'
   content

46   How was the Earthworm employed?
   a) Farmers paid thousands to have him soften the
   soil on their farms
   b) He spoke commercials for women's face creams on
   television
   c) He was a brilliant tightrope walker in a famous circus

47 Why was the City so grateful to the Glow-worm?
   a) Because she became the light inside the torch on the Statue of Liberty
   b) Because she saved the City having to pay a huge electricity bill
   c) Both a) and b)

48 How did Ladybird live happily ever after?
   a) She married the Head of the Fire Department
   b) She became Chief Adviser to the Department of Agriculture
   c) She was elected President of the Nine-spotted Ladybird Society

49 What happened to the peach stone?
   a) It became the chief exhibit in the Museum of Natural History
   b) It became a monument on the lawn of the White House
   c) It was set up in a place of honour in Central Park

50 Why was James not sad and lonely any more?
   a) Because he now had all the friends and playmates in the world
   b) Because he had lots of books to read
   c) Because New York was so exciting

The BFG

1   What is the name of the girl in the BFG?
   a) Elizabeth
   b) Sophie
   c) Mary

2   What was the BFG doing when she saw him?
   a) Eating two children
   b) Jumping over the chimneys
   c) Blowing a trumpet through the Goochey children's
   window

3   Where did the BFG live?
   a) In a house
   b) In a cave
   c) In a burrow

4   What did the girl think the BFG was going to
do to her?
   a) Eat her
   b) Flick her away like a fly
   c) Put her in a glass jar

5   In the BFG's cave, what were the shelves full of?

a) Silver stars
b) Gold bars
c) Glass jars

6   What does the Bonecrunching Giant have for supper every night?

a) Twenty succulent sweet peas
b) Twelve Mexican jumping beans
c) Two wopsey whiffling human beans

7   Bonecruncher prefers juicier and more scrumdiddlyumptious human beans from what country?
  a) *Buffalo in the USA — they taste of steak*
  b) *Turkey — they taste of turkey*
  c) *Switzerland — they taste of cream cheese*

8   Why does no giant ever eat Greeks?
  a) *They are too salty*
  b) *They are too greasy*
  c) *The giants can't catch them*

9   What do human beans from Panama taste of?
  a) *Hats*
  b) *Bananas*
  c) *Pancakes*

10   Who, according to the BFG, has a most
disgustable woolly tickle on the tongue?
   a) Human beans from Cardigan
   b) Human beans from Woolwich
   c) Human beans from Jersey

11   What do the people of Wellington taste of?
   a) Shoes
   b) Boots
   c) Trainers

12   What did the BFG think would happen if
Sophie told on him?
   a) He would be put in a zoo
   b) He would be hunted
   c) He would be interviewed on television

13   What race taste wonderfully of crodscollop?
   a) The French
   b) The English
   c) The Finns

14 How many giants, apart from the BFG, were there?

a) *Seven*
b) *Nine*
c) *Eleven*

15 What tastes like a lovely ice-cream lolly to a giant?

a) *A shivering Swede*
b) *A nice fat Esquimo*
c) *A chilly Canadian*

16 What food hots a cold giant up?

a) *A spicy Chinese*
b) *A curried Indian*
c) *A Hottentot*

17 Who ran the orphanage Sophie lived in?

a) *Miss Trunchbull*
b) *Mrs Clonkers*
c) *Mrs Badlot*

18   What would the BFG love to ride on?
   a) An aeroplane
   b) An elefunt
   c) A boat

19   What kind of giant was the BFG?
   a) A man-eating giant
   b) A grass-gobbling giant
   c) A dream-blowing giant

20   With what does the BFG catch dreams?
   a) With a jar
   b) With a net
   c) With glue

21   What did the BFG think was disgusterous, sickable, rotsome and maggotwise?
   a) Snozzcumber
   b) Humplecrump
   c) Crumpscoddle

22   Where did Sophie hide when the Bloodbottler searched the cave?
   a) Under the table
   b) In the snozzcumber
   c) Behind a glass jar

23   How did Sophie get out of the Bloodbottler's mouth?
   a) She jumped
   b) He spat her out
   c) He yawned and she fell out

24   What do human beans from Chile taste like?
   a) Very chilly
   b) Like icepops
   c) Spicy

25   What flavour do English school-chiddlers have?
   a) Bacon
   b) A nice inky-booky flavour
   c) Cucumbers

26   What do giants drink?
   a) Scobfrottle
   b) Frobscottle
   c) Bloodbeer

27   Why is it a catasterous disastrophe if the bubbles in drinks go up?
   a) Because they cause a rotsome noise
   b) Because they cause a filthsome belchy burp
   c) Because they cause a beastly buzzwangle

28   A whizzpopper is a rude noise caused by bubbles in your tummy going downwards until they have to come out.
   True or false?

29   What is whizzpopping a sign of?
   a) Too many bubbles
   b) Happiness
   c) Overeating

30　What happened to the BFG when he whizzpopped?
  a) Bubbles came out of his mouth
  b) He was lifted clear off his feet, like a rocket
  c) He turned green

31　What did the Fleshlumpeater want to know from the BFG?
  a) Why he liked vegetables
  b) Where he went in the daytime
  c) If he had any frobscottle

32   What did the giants do to the BFG when they caught him?
   a) They bit him
   b) They chased him
   c) They used him as a football

33   How does the Meatdripping Giant prefer to catch human beans?
   a) When they are swimming in the sea
   b) By pretending he is a tree in the park
   c) By grabbing them through the window

34   What is a golden phizzwizard?
   a) A winksquiffler
   b) A very good dream
   c) A tasty snozzcumber

35   What is a trogglehumping, bogthumping grobswitcher?
   a) A nasty giant
   b) A deadly insect
   c) A screaming nightmare

36   Which giant did the BFG give the trogglehumper nightmare to?
   a) Manhugger
   b) Maidmasher
   c) Fleshlumpeater

37   What, according to the BFG, are quogwinkles?
   a) Sweet dreams
   b) Snails
   c) Visitors from the stars

38   Why has the Queen of England not yet been guzzled by Fleshlumpeater?
   a) Because she is guarded by soldiers in big black furry hats
   b) Because she is lucky
   c) Because she was on holiday when he looked for her

39   How does the BFG mix his dreams?
   a) He shakes the jar
   b) He uses an egg-beater
   c) He stirs them with his finger

40   How did Sophie travel back to England with the BFG?
   a) In his ear
   b) In his pocket
   c) In his suitcase

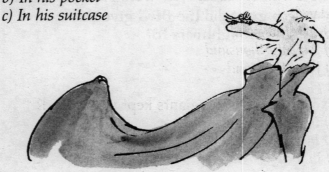

41 Where did the BFG have breakfast in the Palace?
   a) In the Queen's bedroom
   b) In the Great Ballroom
   c) On the lawn

42 What kind of taste do the Swedes of Sweden have?
   a) Sweet and sour
   b) Chilly and chutney
   c) Cheesy

43 Which giant woke up before he could be captured?
   a) Bonecruncher
   b) Childchewer
   c) Fleshlumpeater

44 How many dream jars were brought back to England?
   a) Ten thousand
   b) Twenty thousand
   c) Fifty thousand

45 Where were the giants kept in England?
   a) In a zoo
   b) In a huge pit
   c) In a cage

46   What did the Queen give the BFG?
   a) Money
   b) A special house
   c) Snozzcumbers

47   What title did the BFG get?
   a) The Queen's Giant
   b) The Giants' Keeper
   c) The Royal Dream-Blower

48   What notice did the head keeper put over the giants' pit?
   a) Danger
   b) It is forbidden to feed the giants
   c) Keep off the grass

49   Who gave the BFG special lessons?
   a) The Queen
   b) Sophie
   c) The King of Sweden

50   What did the BFG do in his spare time?
   a) Read books
   b) Painted
   c) Planted snozzcumbers

The Witches

1   Why are Real Witches so hard to catch?
    a) They can disappear into thin air
    b) They are invisible
    c) They look so ordinary

2   What does a Real Witch think about all day?
    a) Great plans to take over the world
    b) The ingredients for foul and wicked spells
    c) How to get rid of children

3   What is the motto of all witches?
    a) All hail to the Grand High Witch
    b) Power to the witches!
    c) Squish them and squiggle them and make them
disappear

4   How many Real Witches are there in England?
    a) About one hundred
    b) About fifty
    c) About five hundred

5   What happened to the boy's parents?
   a) *They disappeared during a world tour*
   b) *They were killed in a car crash*
   c) *They were turned into stone by a witch*

6   What happened to Ranghild Hansen?
   a) *She was given disappearing chocolate by an old lady*
   b) *She went away with a tall lady in white gloves*
   c) *She turned into a yellow bird and flew away*

7   What happened to Solveg Christiansen?
   a) *She became part of an oil painting*
   b) *She turned into a garden gnome*
   c) *She turned into a horse and won the Derby*

8   What happened to Birgit Svenson?
  a) She turned into an umbrella stand
  b) She turned into a cabbage
  c) She turned into a large white chicken

9   What happened to Harald?
  a) He turned into a granite statue
  b) He turned into a turtle
  c) He swam away as a swordfish

10   What became of young Leif?
  a) He turned into a little sail-boat
  b) He turned into a porpoise
  c) He turned into a merman

11   Why do Real Witches always wear gloves?
  a) Because they have claws instead of finger-nails
  b) Because everything they touch withers and dies
  c) Because their skin is extremely delicate and sensitive

12   Why do Real Witches always wear wigs?
  a) As a disguise, so they can change wig and make a quick getaway
  b) Because their own hair is nasty, long, black and scrawny-looking
  c) Because they are bald

13   What problem do wigs cause for witches?
  a) They go a bit fuzzy when you brush them
  b) They are in great danger of falling off on a windy day
  c) They cause wig-rash

14　Why do Real Witches have larger nose-holes?
　　a) *The better to smell children with*
　　b) *To identify other witches*
　　c) *Both a) and b)*

15　Why should sensible children bathe only once a month?
　　a) *Because good clean dirt is healthy*
　　b) *The dirtier you are, the less you smell to a witch*
　　c) *Too much soap dries the skin*

16　How do clean children smell to witches?
　　a) *Like fresh dogs' droppings*
　　b) *Like a large cowpat*
　　c) *Like an enormous mountain of horse manure*

17　What other signs of being a witch are there?
　　a) *The eyebrows always meet in the middle*
　　b) *The dot in the middle of the eyes changes colour*
　　c) *The nose always hooks down at the tip*

18　Why do witches have difficulty wearing pointed shoes?
　　a) *Because they squash their claws*
　　b) *Because witches have only two broad toes, like a camel*
　　c) *Because witches have no toes at all*

19　What colour is a witch's spit?
　　a) *Blue*
　　b) *Rainbow-coloured*
　　c) *Black as coal dust*

20   Which witches are probably the most vicious in the world?
   a) *Russian witches*
   b) *Norwegian witches*
   c) *English witches*

21   How do American witches get parents to eat their own children?
   a) *They turn them into tasty burgers*
   b) *They turn them into hot-dogs*
   c) *They turn them into French fried onions*

22   How often do the witches meet?
   a) *Once a year*
   b) *Once a month*
   c) *Once every five years*

23   What machine does the Grand High Witch have in her headquarters?
   a) A world network computer
   b) A money-printing machine
   c) A satellite communicator

24   Where was the boy when he met his first witch?
   a) In his tree-house
   b) On the way home from school
   c) In the sweet shop

25   Where did the boy and his grandmother go on holiday?
   a) Bournemouth
   b) Blackpool
   c) The Costa del Sol

26   Who are William and Mary?
   a) His best friends at school
   b) His two pet mice
   c) The present king and queen of England

27   What group or society name did the witches use when they held their Annual General Meeting?
   a) The Save the Children Fund
   b) The Keep our Children Safe Association
   c) The RSPCC, or Royal Society for the Prevention of Cruelty to Children

28   Where was the boy hiding at the witches'
meeting?
   a) Under a chair near the fire exit
   b) Under a table covered by a long tablecloth
   c) Behind a screen at the back of the room

29   How did the boy guess the audience in the
ballroom were all witches?
   a) They were all wearing square-toed shoes
   b) They all had noses that hooked down at the tip
   *c) They were all scratching away at the hairs on the
   backs of their necks*

30   Who suddenly appeared on the platform in
the ballroom?
   a) The Grand High Witch
   b) The Grand High Wizard
   c) The Hotel Manager

31   What did the Grand High Witch order the witches of England to do?
 a) To attend a three-week revision course at the end of the month
 b) To get rid of every single child in England within a year
 c) To drink a new special potion to increase their powers

32   What happened to the witch who dared to argue with the Grand High Witch?
 a) She was rocketed through the ceiling
 b) The ground opened up and swallowed her
 c) She was frizzled like a fritter in her chair

33   What was the Grand High Witch's greatest magical recipe?
 a) Opus 34 Child-Disappearing potion
 b) Maggie McGillicuddy's Magic 'Missing' Mix
 c) Formula 86 Delayed Action Mouse-Maker

34   What part of the recipe makes a child become very small?
   a) *The tails of forty-five brown mice that have been cut off with a carving knife*
   b) *The wrong end of a telescope, boiled*
   c) *The small hand of an alarm clock*

35   What is the ingredient that causes the Delayed Action?
   a) *A roasted alarm-clock*
   b) *A stop watch deep-fried*
   c) *A clock with no hands*

36   What do the following have in common: a gruntle's egg, a crabcruncher, a blabbersnitch and a catspringer?
   a) *They are all found on a remote island*
   b) *They are all part of the Grand High Witch's formula*
   c) *They are all spongy and slimy and foul*

37   What did the Grand High Witch promise Bruno Jenkins?
   a) *A whole farm of insects*
   b) *Five cream cakes*
   c) *Six bars of chocolate*

38 What did Bruno Jenkins like
doing more than anything else?
  *a) Eating sweets and roasting ants through his
  magnifying-glass*
  b) Eating cakes and trapping mice
  c) Eating pancakes and collecting beetles in glass jars

39 What did the Grand High Witch do to Bruno
Jenkins?
  a) She crunched him like a carrot
  b) She turned him into a brown mouse
  c) She puffed him into a cloud of blue smoke

40 What did the boy think when he had been
turned into a mouse?
  a) That it was not a bad thing after all
  b) That he would be able to scare lots of people now
  c) That it would be so easy to get into a cookie jar

41　Why did the boy sneak into the Grand High Witch's room?
  a) To get her passport number
  b) To get her little black notebook
  c) To steal a bottle of formula

42　Where did the Grand High Witch hide the bottles of formula?
  a) In her stocking drawer
  b) Inside her mattress
  c) In a tiny safe

43　Who did the boy-mouse meet in the Grand High Witch's room?
  a) Three frogs
  b) Three more mouse-children
  c) Four newts

44   What happened to the boy-mouse in the
kitchen?
   a) The tip of his tail was cut off
   b) He was fried in oil with the chips
   c) He fell into the witch's soup

45   What happened to the witches?
   *a) They were frozen solid by a special task force's
   secret ice-ray gun*
   *b) Their wigs all went up in flames and they were
   sizzled like sausages*
   c) They were all turned into mice

46   Where did the boy-mouse and his
grandmother go?
   a) To America
   b) To Norway
   c) To Germany

47   How many heartbeats does a mouse have per
minute?
   a) Two hundred
   b) Three hundred
   c) Five hundred

48 Why did the boy-mouse not mind being a mouse?

  a) *Because somebody loved him*
  b) *Because he did not have to go to school*
  c) *Because he could get into any place he liked without being seen*

49 How will the boy-mouse and his grandmother get the names and addresses of all the witches in the world?

  a) *From the Hotel Magnificent's register*
  b) *From the Grand High Witch's address book, left in the hotel*
  c) *From the Grand High Witch's Castle*

50 How will they spend the rest of their lives?

  a) *Happily, in Grandmother's specially adapted house in Norway*
  b) *Travelling the world, destroying witches*
  c) *Lecturing and training anti-witch groups*

Answers

Revolting Rhymes

Cinderella

1   b) and c) Because the real one was much more gory, and to keep the children happy

2   b) Because the beautiful Cinderella danced with him

3   b) In her underwear

4   c) It was flushed down the loo

5   c) He chopped off her head

6   c) He chopped off her head

7   c) 'Off with her nut!'

8   b) A decent man

Jack and the Beanstalk

1   a) As old as billy-o

2   b) Plain green

3   b) She threw it on the rubbish dump

4   a) She beat him with the handle of the vacuum cleaner

5   b) A giant with a clever nose

6   c) She was eaten by the giant

7   c) A bath

8   c) Clean between his toes

Snow-White and the Seven Dwarfs

1   b) He put advertisements in every magazine

2   c) A magic, talking looking-glass

3   c) The day she became number two

4   c) Both a) and b)

5   b) She hitched a ride into the city

6   b) General cook and parlour-maid

7   a) They gambled

8   b) No – they were millionaires

Goldilocks and the Three Bears

1   b) A brazen little crook

2   b) Breakfast-time

3   a) A nosey thieving little louse

4   c) Antiques

5   b) Elizabethan

6   b) 'What a lousy chair!'

7   b) Something that a dog had done

8   b) To have baby bear eat her up to get his porridge back

Little Red Riding Hood and the Wolf

1   b) He went and knocked on Grandma's door

2   a) She was tough

3   c) Both a) and b)

4   b) Caviare

5   a) What big teeth you have

6   c) Before she whipped the pistol from her knickers

7   b) A lovely furry wolfskin coat

The Three Little Pigs

1   a) A pig who is a fool

2   b) The tail

3   b) He simply liked indulging

4   a) He was bright and brainy

5   a) He'd blow it up

6   c) Miss Red Riding Hood

7   a) She had just begun to wash her hair

8   a) Spit

Dirty Beasts

The Pig

1   a) England

2   a) What life was really all about

3   c) The pork to make a roast

4   a) Farmer Bland

5   b) He ate him up from head to toe

6   c) An hour

7   c) Because he feared the worst

The Crocodile

1   b) Six juicy children

2   c) Three of each

3   a) Mustard

4   c) Butterscotch and caramel

5   b) When boys are hot and girls are sweet

6   c) Greasy greenish

The Lion

1   c) A lot of red and tender meat

2   a) You

The Scorpion

1   a) Stingaling

2   c) England

3   a) Scowling and murderous

4   c) His long and crinkly tail

5   a) Upon your rump

The Ant-Eater

1   a) He was most dreadfully spoiled

2   b) A giant ant-eater

3   a) An Indian gent

4   b) A bit of meat

5   b) He ate her

6   c) He had him for dessert

The Porcupine

1   a) Saturday

2   b) A great big bag of raspberry creams

3   True

4   c) The dentist

5   a) Fifty guineas

The Cow

1   a) Miss Milky Daisy

2   c) She had two lumps quite near her rump

3   c) She had a pair of gold and silver wings

4   a) Afghanistan

5   c) She dropped a cowpat on his head

The Toad and the Snail

1   a) As large as a fair-sized fattish pig

2   c) To take a ride on his back

3   a) Above the Cliffs of Dover

4   a) To guzzle frogs-legs fried in dripping

5   c) A wonderfully enormous snail

6   b) The enchanting Roly-Poly Bird

The Tummy Beast

1   a) Sugar buns

2   b) To raid the biscuit tin

3   c) Both a) and b)

4   b) He said he would twist the boy's guts

5   a) She fainted

The Magic Finger

1   a) Two

2   c) Philip and William

3   a) Animals and birds

4   c) Both a) and b)

5   b) A young deer

6   c) Both a) and b)

7   a) She grew whiskers and a tail

8   b) No, never at all

9   c) When the girl gets cross and sees red

10   c) Both a) and b)

11   a) Sixteen

12   b) They kept flying around and around, following them

13   c) To get firewood

14   b) Because four ducks were flying around and around the house

15   c) Both a) and b)

16   a) He was the size of a tiny little man

17   b) She was not tall enough to see into it

18   a) They were about as big as robins

19   a) They flew out of the window

20   b) Four enormous ducks with arms

21   c) That they would be eaten by cats and foxes

22   b) A nest

23   a) With their mouths

24   a) Leaves and feathers

25   c) 'I feel I might lay an egg any moment'

26   a) That nobody could hurt them

27   b) A tin of biscuits

28   a) They would fly in
through the window when the
ducks were not looking

29   b) All the windows and
doors were closed

30   c) Both a) and b)

31   b) Apples

32   c) A great wind began to
blow and it rained all night

33   a) Seeing the ducks pointing
guns at him and his family

34   c) Six

35   c) Both a) and b)

36   b) The nest

37   c) Both a) and b)

38   b) They danced with joy

39   c) Four wild ducks

40   c) Both a) and b)

41   b) Feeding birds

42   b) Mr and Mrs Egg

43   c) The nest

44   b) The mess in the
bathroom

45   b) A loud bang

46   c) The tip of her finger began
tingling

47   a) That they would be
nesting in trees that night

The Twits

1   a) How often do they wash their faces

2   a) His forehead, eyes and nose

3   a) Terrifically wise and grand

4   c) A bigger twit than ever

5   b) In spikes, like the bristles of a nailbrush

6   a) Never

7   a) They cannot eat anything without leaving some of the food clinging to the hairs

8   c) Both a) and b)

9   b) A foul and smelly old man, who was also extremely horrid

10   b) She had ugly thoughts

11   c) So that she could hit things with it

12   c) She had a glass eye that was always looking the other way

13   b) Mrs Twit's glass eye

14   a) He put a large frog in her bed

15   a) She fainted

16   b) She made Squiggly Spaghetti, with worms

17   a) He put little extra pieces on to the end of her walking-stick

18   c) He tied her feet down and attached sixty gas-filled balloons to the top half of her body

19   a) Mrs Twit

20   b) She bit through their strings and slowly released the balloons so she could float down

21   b) Mrs Twit herself

22   a) It had no windows

23   c) A mass of thistles and stinging-nettles

24   b) Bird Pie

25   c) For catching birds

26   a) Four little boys

27   b) They slipped out of their pants and tumbled to the ground

28   b) To own an upside-down monkey circus

29   c) To eat and drink

30   c) Both a) and b)

31   a) Africa

32   b) To warn the other birds about The Big Dead Tree glue

33   c) Both a) and b)

34   a) They went to buy shotguns

35   b) The Roly-Poly Bird

36   a) To make them stand upside-down for hours and hours

37   a) To cover the ceiling with glue

38   c) Both a) and b)

39   a) By using Hugtight glue, the strongest glue in the world

40   c) Turning all the pictures upside-down

41   b) They had to go inside to load up the guns

42   b) Hugtight glue

43   a) Mr Twit

44   b) A tree-house

45   a) They built their nests around the tree-house to conceal it

46   c) They flew Roly-Poly Super Jet

47   a) It disappeared into the fatty folds of his flabby neck

48   c) They got the Dreaded Shrinks and disappeared

49   b) Fred, the gas-meter reader

50   c) 'Hooray!'

James and the Giant Peach

1   b) He was four

2   c) They were eaten up by an enormous angry rhinoceros

3   a) It was by the sea

4   b) Aunt Sponge and Aunt Spiker

5   a) They were selfish and lazy and cruel

6   c) Both a) and b)

7   b) She was lean and tall and bony

8   b) A small man in a dark-green suit

9   c) Things that looked like green stones or crystals which were made of crocodile tongues

10   c) Ten hairs from his own head

11   a) He spilled them all over the place when he fell flat on his face

12   a) Down into the earth round the peach tree

13   b) Aunt Spiker

14   b) 'Terrifico! Magnifico! Splendifico!'

15   c) One shilling

16   c) Locked up in his bedroom

17   a) They ordered him to go outside to clean up all the rubbish people had left behind

18   c) Both a) and b)

19   a) Through a door at the end of a tunnel

20   a) They were as big as James himself

21   b) He thought, when they said they were hungry, that they wanted to eat him

22   a) The Ladybird telling him to stop pulling the Earthworm's leg

23   b) The Spider

24   b) Lady fireflies without wings

25   a) The Centipede nibbled away the stem

26   a) With a crunch, they were ironed out as flat as a couple of paper dolls

27   c) When, with a loud smack, it hit the water

28   a) The Earthworm

29   b) It was attacked by sharks

30   a) By lifting it out of the water

31   b) Five hundred and two

32   c) Queen Mary

33   a) A violin

34   b) One on each side of his tummy

35   c) Cloud-Men

36   b) The Centipede's insults

37   b) Her bulb was broken

38   a) Painting a rainbow

39   b) He was entirely covered by a gallon of thick purple paint

40   b) The biggest bomb in the world

41   a) On the pinnacle of the Empire State Building

42   a) Six big strong men fainted

43   b) James appeared and said, 'Hello, everybody!'

44   c) Because juice was leaking out from the peach and spilling on to the road

45   c) A long trail of children ate the peach to their hearts' content

46   b) He spoke commercials for women's face creams on television

47   c) Both a) and b)

48   a) She married the Head of the Fire Department

49   c) It was set up in a place of honour in Central Park

50   a) Because he now had all the friends and playmates in the world

The BFG

1   b) Sophie

2   c) Blowing a trumpet through the Goochey children's window

3   b) In a cave

4   a) Eat her

5   c) Glass jars

6   c) Two wopsey whiffling human beans

7   b) Turkey — they taste of turkey

8   b) They are too greasy

9   a) Hats

10   c) Human beans from Jersey

11   b) Boots

12   a) He would be put in a zoo

13   b) The English

14   b) Nine

15   b) A nice fat Esquimo

16   c) A Hottentot

17   b) Mrs Clonkers

18   b) An elefunt

19   c) A dream-blowing giant

20   b) With a net

21   a) Snozzcumber

22   b) In the snozzcumber

23   b) He spat her out

24   a) Very chilly

25   b) A nice inky-booky flavour

26   b) Frobscottle

27   b) Because they cause a filthsome belchy burp

28   True

29   b) Happiness

30   b) He was lifted clear off his feet, like a rocket

31   b) Where he went in the daytime

32   c) They used him as a football

33   b) By pretending he is a tree in the park

34   b) A very good dream

35   c) A screaming nightmare

36   c) Fleshlumpeater

37   c) Visitors from the stars

38   a) Because she is guarded by soldiers in big black furry hats

39   b) He uses an egg-beater

40   a) In his ear

41   b) In the Great Ballroom

42   a) Sweet and sour

43   c) Fleshlumpeater

44   c) Fifty thousand

45   b) In a huge pit

46   b) A special house

47   c) The Royal Dream-Blower

48   b) It is forbidden to feed the giants

49   b) Sophie

50   a) Read books

The Witches

1   c) They look so ordinary

2   c) How to get rid of children

3   c) Squish them and squiggle them and make them disappear

4   a) About one hundred

5   b) They were killed in a car crash

6   b) She went away with a tall lady in white gloves

7   a) She became part of an oil painting

8   c) She turned into a large white chicken

9   a) He turned into a granite statue

10   b) He turned into a porpoise

11   a) Because they have claws instead of finger-nails

12   c) Because they are bald

13   c) They cause wig-rash

14   a) The better to smell children with

15   b) The dirtier you are, the less you smell to a witch

16   a) Like fresh dogs' droppings

17   b) The dot in the middle of the eyes changes colour

18   c) Because witches have no toes at all

19   a) Blue

20   c) English witches

21   b) They turn them into hot-dogs

22   a) Once a year

23   b) A money-printing machine

24   a) In his tree-house

25   a) Bournemouth

26   b) His two pet mice

27   c) The RSPCC, or Royal Society for the Prevention of Cruelty to Children

28   c) Behind a screen at the back of the room

29   c) They were all scratching away at the hairs on the backs of their necks

30   a) The Grand High Witch

31   b) To get rid of every single child in England within a year

32   c) She was frizzled like a fritter in her chair

33   c) Formula 86 Delayed Action Mouse-Maker

34   b) The wrong end of a telescope, boiled

35   a) A roasted alarm-clock

36   b) They are all part of the Grand High Witch's formula

37   c) Six bars of chocolate

38   a) Eating sweets and roasting ants through his magnifying-glass

39   b) She turned him into a brown mouse

40   a) That it was not a bad thing after all

41   c) To steal a bottle of formula

42   b) Inside her mattress

43   a) Three frogs

44   a) The tip of his tail was cut off

45   c) They were all turned into mice

46   b) To Norway

47   c) Five hundred

48   a) Because somebody loved him

49   c) From the Grand High Witch's Castle

50   b) Travelling the world, destroying witches